Preface

Every country has its own aural traditions of myth and legend, and the stories in this series come from the four corners of the earth. They will help the modern child to appreciate how happenings may be interpreted in different ways by people whose entire way of thinking may, for many reasons, be different.

The series is intended for an age range of 7 + to 11 +, with more easily understood stories in the first two books and more difficult concepts in the two later books.

Harry Stanton
Audrey Daly

Contents

WIDE RANGE

Myths and Legends

2

**Harry Stanton
and Audrey Daly**

Oliver & Boyd

*Illustrated by Tony Herbert, Ray Mutimer,
John Harrold and Michael Strand*

OLIVER & BOYD
Robert Stevenson House
1–3 Baxter's Place
Leith Walk
Edinburgh EH1 3BB

A Division of Longman Group Ltd

First published 1984

ISBN 0 05 003361 1

Set in Monophoto Plantin 14/20pt
Printed in Hong Kong by
Wing King Tong Printing Co. Ltd

Theseus and the Minotaur

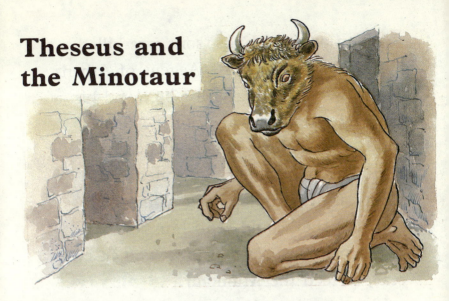

King Minos of Crete was a powerful
ruler and a cruel man. Beneath his
palace, he kept a strange pet called
the Minotaur. It was a monster with
the body of a man and the head of a
bull, and it was fed on human flesh.

The Minotaur was kept in a maze or
labyrinth of narrow passages below the
palace. There was only one way into
the labyrinth, and those who went in
never came out again. They were
either eaten by the Minotaur, or died
trying to find their way out.

When one of Minos' sons was killed
by the soldiers of King Aegeus of Athens,
Minos was very angry, for he loved his
son. He went to war against Athens,
and defeated them. Then instead of
burning down the city of Athens and
killing all its people, King Minos
said that they could send him seven
young men and seven young women every
year, to feed the Minotaur.

If at any time they refused, King
Minos would attack Athens once more.

King Aegeus and the people of Athens
were frightened of Minos, for they knew
he would do as he said. So every year,
they chose seven young men and seven
young women to be sent to the Minotaur.

King Aegeus had a son called Theseus,
who grew up strong and brave. When he
was told the story, he said to his father,

"This year *I'll* be one of the young
men, and I will kill the Minotaur."

His father could not stop him, so

with the other young people, Theseus set off for Crete in a ship with black sails.

As the brave young man went aboard the ship Aegeus said,

"I will watch from the top of the cliffs every day you are away. If you kill the Minotaur, put white sails on the ship. Then as soon as I see them I shall know that you are safe."

When they landed in Crete, Minos was told that Theseus was the son of the king of Athens. He laughed loudly, but his daughter Ariadne did not laugh. She had fallen in love with Theseus, and had made up her mind to help him.

That night she went to Theseus and said, "I will help you to kill the Minotaur if you will take me back to Athens as your wife."

Theseus agreed, for Ariadne was very beautiful.

She gave Theseus a sword
and a large ball of thread, then
she took him to the door of the
labyrinth where the Minotaur was kept.

"Tie one end of the thread to the
door, and carry the ball of thread
with you," she said. "When you
have killed the Minotaur,
the thread will help you to find
your way back."

Theseus thanked her. He tied the
thread to the door, then set off into
the labyrinth to find the monster.

Slowly he moved forward in the
half-light, letting the thread out
behind him. There were many different
passages, going in all directions,
and sometimes he came to a blank
wall and had to find his way round it.

Further and further he went
and the ball of thread grew smaller
and smaller. Then somewhere in the
distance he began to hear the monster

breathing and snorting. Theseus
knew that the Minotaur must be very
near now.

Just as the last piece of thread
unwound, he saw the monster.

It was a huge, terrifying creature.
As Theseus crept forward, sword in
hand, its wicked eyes shone red
in the half-light.

Suddenly it saw him, lowered its
head and charged. Theseus jumped
to one side and the Minotaur's

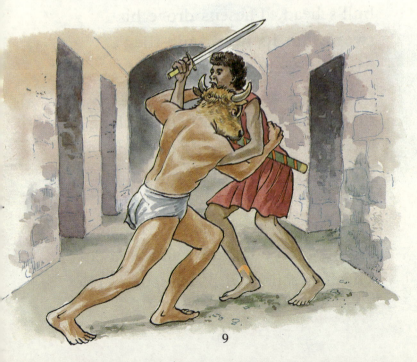

horns just missed his chest.

It turned swiftly and charged again, reaching out for him with its hairy arms. Theseus jumped to one side once more, then drove his sword deep into the monster's side.

Again and again the Minotaur charged, and each time Theseus thrust his sword into its body. At last, mad with pain and fury, it charged at the wall. As it stood there dazed, shaking its great bull's head, Theseus drove his sword into its heart, and the Minotaur fell dead at his feet.

Now Theseus pulled on the thread, and followed it back along the dark passages until he came to the door of the labyrinth.

Princess Ariadne was waiting for him, and together they hurried to find the young men and women who had sailed with Theseus. They

all wanted to ask questions about
the Minotaur, but there was no time.

Quickly they followed Ariadne
through secret passages until they
reached their ship.   Then they sailed
silently away from Crete.   Ariadne
went with them, happy that Theseus
was safe.

Fighting the Minotaur had made
Theseus very tired, and for three
days and nights he slept without waking.

While he was asleep, the ship
had to stop at an island to get water,
and Princess Ariadne went ashore
to pick wild flowers.

Suddenly a wind sprang up and
dark clouds raced across the sky.
A storm was coming, and the sailors
hurried back to the ship. Forgetting
all about Ariadne, they sailed away
from the island so that the storm
could not blow their ship on to
the rocks.

When they were far out to sea,
the storm woke Theseus from his
deep sleep.

"Where is Princess Ariadne?"
he asked.

She could not be found, for she
had been left behind. Theseus tried
to turn the ship round, but the storm
was blowing them further and further
away from the island.

Ariadne never saw Theseus again.
She was very unhappy for a time,
but then the god of wine, Dionysus,
came to her rescue and she
married him.

When Theseus found that he could
not go back for Ariadne, he was so
upset that he forgot to tell the
sailors to put the white sails on the ship.

From high up on the cliffs near
Athens, King Aegeus had been
watching for many weeks to see if
his son would come back. At last
he saw a ship in the distance—
and the sails were black.

Tears filled the king's eyes.
His son Theseus was dead. Sadly
he turned to go home. He did not

look where he was going, and he fell
over the edge of the cliff and drowned.

Although they were unhappy at their
king's death, the people of Athens
were very pleased to see Theseus
and the other young people again.

When they told Theseus that his
father had died, he was very sad.
Soon afterwards he became king of
Athens, and he named the sea into
which his father had fallen, the
Aegean Sea, in his memory.

And when he heard of Ariadne's
marriage to Dionysus, he held a
wine festival in their honour.

Daedalus and Icarus

In the days of King Minos,
a famous man called Daedalus lived
on Crete. He was a very clever man
who made many things for the king.
One of these things was the maze
or labyrinth beneath the palace
in which the Minotaur lived
before it was killed by Theseus.

King Minos was so pleased with
the things that Daedalus made
for him that he did not want him
to leave the island of Crete.
When Daedalus said that he and
his son Icarus wanted to go to
Sicily, King Minos flew into a rage.

"If you try to get away,
I shall put you in the maze
with the Minotaur," he said.

This made Daedalus want to
get away even more. He could

not get away by ship, however, because the king had men watching all the ships that left the island.

Daedalus thought and thought, until one day he had an idea.

He was watching some gulls flying over the sea, and he suddenly knew how he and Icarus could escape. They would fly!

He went straight to his workshop and began making two great pairs of wings—one pair for himself and one pair for Icarus.

When they were finished, he fastened one pair of wings on his own shoulders, and the other pair on his son's shoulders.

"Now," he said to Icarus, "you must be careful. You mustn't fly too high. If you do, you may fly too close to the sun and it will melt the wax which holds the wings together."

Together they walked slowly
to the cliffs, because the wings
were heavy.   Then they moved them
up and down once or twice to try them.

Just before they started to fly,
Daedalus said to Icarus,

"Don't forget, you mustn't fly too high."
Soon they were flying above the sea.

Icarus thought flying was great fun.
He flew this way and that, shouting,

"Look at me, look at me!"
Higher and higher he flew, nearer
and nearer the sun.

"Come back, come back!" shouted
Daedalus, but Icarus took no notice.
He went on flying higher and higher,
nearer and nearer the sun.

Soon he flew so high that the sun
melted the wax holding his wings
together.   Icarus began to fall.
He fell down, down, down into the
sea and was drowned.

His father Daedalus was very sad
as he flew on.

At last he landed safely on the
island of Sicily, and he lived
there for the rest of his life.
He never forgot his son, and we
have never forgotten the young
man who flew too near the sun.

The Golden Touch

One evening, as he was walking
in his garden, King Midas found
an untidy old man sitting beside
one of the flower beds.

"You can't sit there," said Midas.
"This is *my* garden."

The old man looked up at him.

"Please forgive me," he said.
"I'm not feeling very well,
and I couldn't walk one more step."

Although he liked his garden
to himself, King Midas was a kind
man. He called his servants, and
they took the old man into the
palace, where they looked after
him until he was better.

Each day the king went to talk
to the old man, and soon discovered
that his name was Silenus, and he
had once taught Dionysus, the
god of wine.

When the old man was better,
Dionysus himself came to the palace,
to take Silenus back to his home.

He was pleased that Midas
had been so kind to his old teacher,
so he said that the king could have
anything he wanted to ask for.

Now as well as being kind,
King Midas was also a very foolish
man. He loved gold more than
anything in the world.

In his palace, he had rooms
and rooms full of boxes which were
all filled with gold.

Dionysus gave him a moment or two
to think about it, then he asked,

"What do you want?"

"I would like every single thing
I touch to turn to gold!" said the king.

Dionysus knew that Midas was
being foolish, but he gave him
his wish, then he took Silenus
back to his home.

King Midas was very happy.
He touched a red rose—and the
rose changed into gold.   The leaves
were gold, the stalk was gold,
even the flower had changed into gold.

The king smiled as he looked at
it, then with the tip of his finger
he touched a small stone.

The small stone turned into gold.

King Midas laughed out loud.
He was very happy.

Behind him was a great oak tree.
The king turned to it and with
the tip of his little finger he
touched one of the leaves.

The whole tree changed into gold.
Every leaf, every twig and every
branch became pure gold!

"I shall be so rich!" said Midas.

For the rest of the day he
walked round the garden and through
the castle, changing everything
in sight to gold.

When he sat down to eat, the
chair, then the table, and even
his plate turned to gold.

As each thing changed, the king
smiled more and more.

But when he picked up an apple,
the apple changed into gold
and he could not eat it. He put
a grape into his mouth—and the
grape turned into a small hard
ball of gold.

King Midas stopped smiling
and became very angry.   He tried
to drink some water.

But there was no water in the
cup, only gold.

Everything that he touched
turned into gold.

"Whatever am I going to do?"
the king asked himself unhappily.
"I shall die if I can't eat or
drink."   He began to understand
that he had been very foolish indeed.

At that moment his little daughter,
the princess, came to see him.   She
ran to hug him—and she changed
into gold.

King Midas stared down at the
little gold figure in his arms,
and tears ran down his cheeks.
What use was all the gold
in the world if he lost his
little daughter?

He ran into the garden
shouting, "Help me! Help me!"
He was looking for Dionysus,
the god who had given him this
terrible gift.

There under a tree sat Dionysus.

He had come back because
he had known that King Midas
would need his help.

"Help me! Help me!" the king
cried again. "I have lost my
little daughter because everything
I touch turns into gold."

"But that's what you asked for,"
said Dionysus.

King Midas hung his head.

"Yes, I've been very foolish," he
said. "I shall give all my gold
away. I don't want any of it any
more. Please change everything
back again."

"All right," said Dionysus.
"I *will* change it all back again,
but you must go down to the river
and wash the magic spell away."

King Midas ran as fast as he
could down to the river. As he
washed himself all over, the banks
of the river turned to gold.

Then he walked slowly back
to the palace. He stopped once
to touch a pink rose—and it
stayed pink. It did not change
into gold.

When he came to his garden,
he found that Dionysus had gone,
and the trees, stones and flowers
were no longer made of gold.

Then there was a happy shout,
"Daddy, Daddy!" and the princess
ran across the garden to meet him.

How the Tortoise got its Shell

Zeus was having a party, and he asked all the animals to come.

The bears and the frogs, the fish and the dogs, the mice and the cats, the birds and the wolves— they all came to his party.

The only animal that did not come to his party was the tortoise— and Zeus was not very pleased about it.

He went to see the tortoise.

"Why didn't you come to my party?" he asked.

"Because I like to stay at home," said the tortoise.

"Then you shall!" said Zeus crossly. "You shall stay at home for ever!"

And ever since that time, the tortoise is always at home, for Zeus put his house on his back.

Iduna and the Golden Apples

Ivaldi the dwarf and his family
lived in a dark gloomy cave
far away in the cold lands
of the North. Ivaldi's sons
were small and ugly, but their
sister Iduna was tall and
beautiful.

Sometimes Iduna would leave
the cave to walk among the flowers,
and there one day she met Bragi,
the happy god of poetry. They
fell in love and married, and he
took her to Asgard, the home
of the gods. All the gods liked
Bragi's new wife, and they gave
her the golden apples to look after.

The golden apples were kept
in a special casket with a special
lock, for their magic powers kept

the gods looking young and handsome
for ever.

One day Bragi's father, Odin,
the king of the gods, went on a
hunting trip. With him was his
brother Honir, and Loki, the god
of fire, who was cunning and sly.

Late in the day, when they were
cooking their dinner, a huge eagle
swooped down and stole some of
the meat. When Loki tried to chase
it off, the eagle picked him up
and carried him away.

Loki was very frightened.

"Who are you?" he cried. "I'm
sure you're not really an eagle."

"I'm Thiazi, the storm giant,"
the eagle replied, "and I've always
hated the gods. I'm going to kill you."

He flew on over a forest,
dragging Loki through the tree-tops.

"Let me go," cried Loki, "and
you can have anything you want."

The eagle did not answer for
a moment. Then he said,

"I will let you go if you promise
to bring Iduna and her golden apples
to me. I too would like to stay young."

"Yes, yes!" shouted Loki. "I promise."

As he spoke, the eagle let him go.
Loki fell on to the mountainside
and rolled all the way to the bottom.

He went back to Odin and Honir,
but he did not tell them about
his promise to the eagle. A promise
that could not be broken.

When the three went back to Asgard, the eagle followed. He waited in the forest nearby for Loki to bring Iduna and her casket of golden apples to him.

The next day Loki went to see Iduna and said,

"I have a surprise for you. I've found another tree on which magic apples grow."

"Oh, that can't be true," replied Iduna.

"I've seen them for myself," said Loki. "The tree is very tall with red leaves, and the fruit is golden."

Iduna was very upset when she heard this. She said,

"Only the gods may eat golden apples. You will have to take me to the tree so that I can pick the apples and bring them here."

"All right," said Loki. "Bring

your casket of apples with you
so that you can make sure the apples
are the same," he added cunningly.

Iduna picked up her casket
of golden apples and went with Loki.
Together they walked from Asgard
across the fields and into the woods.

There Thiazi the storm giant
was waiting, in the form of an eagle,
in the branches of an oak tree.

Silently he flew down and grabbed
Iduna in his great claws.
Then he flew off, taking her
to his castle of Thrymheim,
high up on a clifftop, in the
mountains. There it was so cold
that the trees were heavy with snow,
and wolves howled all day.

When they arrived, the eagle set
her down in the castle courtyard.
Then as she watched, he changed
from an eagle into Thiazi the storm
giant. Iduna cried out in surprise.

"Give me one of your golden apples,"
said Thiazi. "I am Thiazi the
storm giant, and I wish to stay
young for ever."

"No," said Iduna, holding the
casket tightly. "These apples are
only for the gods, and they will
stay in this casket which I alone
can open. I won't give you
even one apple!"

"I shall lock you up in my tower
and leave you there until you
give me one," said Thiazi, looking
down at her.

"No," said Iduna again. "Whatever
you do to me, you won't get any apples."

Her words made Thiazi very angry,
and he locked her up in a high tower
from which she could not escape,
just as he had said he would.

*　　*　　*　　*　　*　　*

That evening the gods in Asgard
noticed that Iduna was not there,
but they thought she was with her
husband Bragi.

Some days went by, and the gods
began to feel older because they
could not eat the golden apples.
Odin's fair hair began to turn grey
and Thor, the strong god of thunder,
found that he was getting weak.

Then Bragi returned—and Iduna
had not been with him.

The gods grew worried.

"We must find her," said Odin.
"Who saw her last?"

For a long time the gods talked,
then Odin's wife remembered.

"I saw Iduna walking with Loki,
and she had her casket of golden
apples with her."

"Where's Loki?" roared Odin.

The gods rushed from the room and
searched the castle.   Not long afterwards
Thor came back, dragging Loki with him.

"Where is Iduna?" demanded Odin.

"Why ask me?" said Loki, with
a sly smile.

Thor shook Loki so hard that
at last he shouted, "Stop!   Stop!"

"Where is Iduna?" roared Odin again.

"Thiazi the storm giant has taken
her away," said Loki.

The gods were very angry.

"Get her back quickly," said Odin, "because without the apples we will all grow old and die."

"I'll try to find her," agreed Loki, because he too hated growing old. With a magic spell, he changed himself into a hawk and said,

"I'll fly to the mountains to find Thiazi's castle, and I'll bring Iduna back."

The gods watched as the hawk flew quickly into the distance.

* * * * * *

Loki flew northwards until he reached the mountains. For many days he searched, until he found Thiazi's castle, high on a clifftop.

He flew round the castle, and at last he saw Iduna's lovely face as she looked out of the window in the tower.

As he flew nearer, he heard her

crying, for she was very unhappy.

When the hawk flew into the room,
she was very frightened.

"Don't be afraid," it said.
"I'm Loki, and I've come to save you."

With a wave of his wing he cast
a magic spell, and changed Iduna
and her casket of golden apples into
a small nut. Then he picked up the
nut in his claws and flew out
through the window.

Thiazi was standing in the
courtyard when Loki flew from the
open window. The storm giant looked

up in surprise, because no birds
ever came near his castle.   Then
he thought,

"Has Iduna been rescued?"

He changed himself into an eagle
again and flew up until he could
see into the room where Iduna had
been held prisoner.

She had escaped!   The storm giant
flew after Loki, who was by now a
long way off.   Loki flew as fast as
he could, but the eagle was faster.

Ever since Loki had left, the gods
had been waiting and watching for
him on the walls of Asgard.
Suddenly, in the distance, they saw
a hawk, with an eagle close behind.
They knew it was Loki, with Thiazi
trying to catch him.

Quickly they set fire to a huge
pile of wood in front of their walls.

As the flames leapt up high in
the air, Loki flew through them.

He was safe, for he was the god of fire.
But the eagle's feathers caught
fire as he followed Loki.   He fell
to the ground and with one blow
of his hammer, Thor killed Thiazi
the storm giant.

Loki set the nut down on the floor
in front of the gods.   He cast
his magic spell, and as they watched
the nut changed into Iduna
and her casket of golden apples.

Her return made the gods happy.
Iduna was back with her friends
and once again the gods could eat
her golden apples and stay young
for ever.

Thor goes Fishing

Thor, the Norse god of thunder, often stayed with his friend, the Giant of the Sea. Although Thor was much smaller, he was just as strong as the giant. From time to time, they went hunting and fishing together.

One evening, after catching a whale, the Giant of the Sea said,

"It's going to be difficult to cook this whale. It's the largest whale I've ever seen."

"Put it in a large cooking pot," said Thor.

"I haven't got a cooking pot large enough. What I need is a really big one. I know the giant Hymir has some large cooking pots, but I'm sure he won't give *me* one!"

"Then *I'll* go and see Hymir and get a large cooking pot for you," said Thor.

Next morning Thor set off to the land where Hymir lived. It was a long way away, and he travelled for many days before he came to the giant's home.

Hymir's house was enormous. The chimneys were hidden in the clouds, and the door was so big that Thor could not even reach the handle!

He lifted his hammer and knocked on the door. After a while, the giant's wife opened it. She was so tall that Thor only came up to her knee.

"Hello, little Thor," she said, looking down at him. "Why have you come to the house of Hymir?"

"The Giant of the Sea has caught

a very large whale, and he would like
one of your large cooking pots,"
replied Thor.

"My husband is away hunting, but
come in and wait for him to return,"
said Hymir's wife, and she opened the
door wide.

"When Hymir comes back,
I'll ask him if you can have a large
cooking pot for the Giant of the Sea,"
she added.

While he was waiting for the giant
to come home, Thor climbed on to a
chair beside the fire and went to sleep.
He was tired after his journey.

Late in the afternoon, he woke up
to hear the giant coming home. The
heavy footsteps made the house shake.

"Hide," said Hymir's wife, "and I
will tell him that you are here."
So Thor hid behind a pile of logs.

The door opened and Hymir came
into the room.

"What's for dinner?" he asked,
and he sniffed the air.
Then he sniffed again.

"There's a strange smell in the
house, and it's not my dinner!"
he shouted. Then he sniffed again
and shouted once more, "Where is he?"

His voice shook the house, and the
cooking pots on the wall fell down.

"It's all right. Thor has come
to see you," said his wife.

"And what does he want?" asked
Hymir.

"He wants a large cooking pot for
the Giant of the Sea," she replied.

"Oh, does he!" roared Hymir.
"Well, come here, little Thor. You
can stop hiding."

Thor walked out from behind
the pile of logs.

"Welcome, little Thor," said
the giant. "So you want one of
my cooking pots! You can only

44

have one if you can prove that you
are as strong as me." Hymir laughed
as he looked down at Thor. Then
he turned to his wife. "Now get
me some food ready."

The giant's wife set the table.
She had cooked three whole oxen
for supper.

"Eat, little Thor, eat,"
boomed the giant.

Thor was very hungry. By the time Hymir and his wife had sat at the table, Thor had eaten two of the oxen. Only one was left for Hymir and his wife.

"You must be hungry!" exclaimed the giant.

"I was, but I'm all right now," replied Thor.

"I must get some more food, or soon there will be nothing left to eat in the house," thought Hymir.

Early next morning Hymir woke early to go fishing. Thor heard the giant dragging a boat down to the sea shore, and went to find out what he was doing.

"Where are you going?" asked Thor.

"I'm going to catch some whales
for breakfast," replied Hymir.

"Can I come with you?" asked Thor.

"You are too small, little Thor!"
laughed Hymir.

"Oh, am I!" cried Thor angrily.

"And it's far too cold for a little
chap like you—you would freeze out
there," teased the giant.

"I'll show you that I can catch
something better than a whale," cried
Thor, growing more and more cross.

"All right, you can come fishing
with me if you want," said Hymir, "but
you'll have to get your own rod
and bait."

Thor jumped over a nearby wall into
a field and pulled a tree out of the
ground to use as a rod. Then he
chopped the head off one of Hymir's
cattle, to use as bait.

As Hymir pushed the boat off from

the shore Thor climbed aboard, carrying his rod and bait. When Hymir saw that the head had been chopped off one of his cattle to use as bait, he was not very pleased.

"I'll row," cried Thor and took the oars. He rowed so hard that Hymir sat down with a bump, and soon became frightened.

"Stop! Stop!" he shouted. "We've rowed far enough. This is a good place to fish."

"No," said Thor. "I want to catch monsters. Here you can only catch tiny fish." He rowed on and on, harder and harder.

Soon they were out of sight of land, and the waves were higher than the boat. Hymir grew even more frightened.

"Don't stop here," he shouted. "This is where the serpent lives."

When Thor heard that, he stopped

rowing. "We'll fish here," he said.

So Hymir threw his line over the side,
and soon he had caught two large whales.

"Now we can go home," he said.

"Wait," said Thor. "Now it's my
turn to fish."

He tied a thick rope to the tree
he was using as a rod, and after putting
the ox's head on a hook, he dropped
it over the side.

Very soon, Thor felt something
tugging at the end of his line.

"What have you got there, little Thor? A sprat or a tadpole?" laughed Hymir, who was feeling brave again.

He did not laugh for long. Thor began to pull in the rope, and suddenly he was dragged half-way out of the boat.

"It's a very big fish!" shouted Thor.

"Perhaps it's a serpent!" cried Hymir.

Thor set his feet against the side of the boat and slowly pulled in his fishing line until the head of a sea serpent came out of the water.

It was the ugliest thing that Hymir had ever seen. Its mouth was full of sharp teeth, and for a moment its evil red eyes stared at him.

"Quick, let it go!" cried the giant. "It will eat us."

Thor pulled the fishing line tighter, and the serpent's tail beat the sea into a white foam. When its tail hit the side of the boat, Thor shouted,

"Hold my rod, and I'll kill
the serpent with my hammer."

But Hymir was too frightened.
Instead, he took out his fishing
knife and cut the line, and the
serpent escaped. Only a white
foam upon the sea showed where
the monster had been.

"You fool!" cried Thor in a
rage. He was so angry that he hit
the giant with his fist and knocked
him into the sea.

Hymir climbed back into the boat,
cold and wet. He sat and sulked
as Thor rowed back to the shore.

When they got back Hymir said,
"You can help me to unload the boat."

"Of course I will," replied Thor,
then he picked up the boat with the
whales and rods still in it, and
carried it to the house.

Hymir could only follow him.

"I've caught two whales for
breakfast," the giant said to his wife.

She cooked the whales and put
them on the table, but before she
and her husband could even sit
down, Thor had eaten both whales.

"You are very greedy!" shouted
the giant.

"I'm not greedy. I eat a lot
because I'm stronger than you," said
Thor. "Now may I have one of your
cooking pots?"

"You aren't stronger than me.
You are just greedy!" said Hymir.

"I've *shown* you that I'm
stronger!" cried Thor.

"You can certainly row very well, and you can fish and carry boats, but I won't believe that you are stronger than me unless you can break this," said the giant, handing Thor a glass cup.

For a moment the god of thunder looked down at the glass cup in his hand. Then he dropped it on to the stone floor. It did not break.

Hymir gave a sly smile as Thor picked up the cup.

"Is it too heavy for you?" he teased.

Thor banged the glass cup on the table—and still it did not break.

The giant laughed.

"It's only made of glass, little Thor. Why can't you break it?"

Growing crosser and crosser, Thor threw the cup at the wall. With a loud crash it went straight through, leaving a hole in the stone wall.

Hymir laughed and laughed, until tears rolled down his face.

"You've broken the wall, but you haven't broken the cup," he cried. "Poor little Thor, poor little Thor."

Hymir's wife was laughing too.

"My husband's head is stronger than that wall," she said as she went to pick up the cup.

Now Thor knew what he had to do.

"Let's see you break the cup. It's only made of glass. How weak you are, little Thor," the giant went on teasing him.

But he did not laugh for long.
Thor lifted the glass cup and threw
it with all his strength at the
giant's head.   It broke into
tiny pieces.

Hymir stopped laughing and put
his hand to his head.

"That hurt!" he said unhappily.
"And you've broken my cup.   It was
the only cup I had."

But Thor took no notice.   "*Now*
can I have a cooking pot?" he asked.

"Oh, take one, take one," said
Hymir.   "Take the biggest one if
you like, then go away. Don't come
back to my house ever again."

The giant turned his back on Thor,
went into the corner of the room,
and began to sulk.

"Thank you," said Thor.   He looked
for the giant's largest cooking pot,
picked it up, and took it to his
friend, the Giant of the Sea.

The King of the Frogs

Deep in the forest was a pool
where the frogs lived. Only frogs
lived there, and it was like a
little country all by itself.

They had a quiet, happy life.
Then one day, when they were talking
together, a frog said,

"We should have a king in our pool."

So they went to Zeus and asked
him to give them a king.

Zeus looked down at them and
laughed. Then he took a log of
wood and threw it into the pool.

One by one the frogs swam up
to the log of wood and looked at it.

Some of the frogs swam under it.

"Our new king is very quiet,"
said one.

Then another frog swam up to
the log and climbed on top of it.
The rest of the frogs looked up
at him, and after a while they all
climbed on to the log.

For a week the frogs played with
the log of wood, and at last grew
tired of it.

"He is much too quiet," they said,
and they went to see Zeus again.

"Our king is too quiet," they said.
"We want a better one!"

"Then I shall give you another one,"
said Zeus, growing cross with them.

The next day he brought a stork to the pool.

The frogs were very pleased, and went together to meet their new king.

Then the stork with his long beak began to eat up the frogs, one by one.

"We want another king," shouted the frogs that were left.

"You have got what you asked for," replied Zeus. And then he went away.

Ilya of Muron

Ilya came from the city of Muron in
the south of Russia. He was a brave
knight, and he spent his whole life
riding along on his white horse,
looking for adventures.

When Ilya was growing old, he went
on a journey to a part of the country
where he had never been before. All
the roads were strange to him. After
a few days, he came to a crossroads
where there were three signposts, and
he stopped, wondering which way to go.

The signpost which pointed to the west said, "He who rides along this road will die."

The one which pointed to the north said, "He who rides along this road will be married."

"That's a strange signpost," thought Ilya. "I wonder what the third one has on it."

He looked at the board which pointed to the east. Written on it was, "He who rides along this road will be rich."

The old knight sat upon his horse and looked again at the three signposts, one after the other.

Then he said to himself, "I *have* a wife and I don't want to be married again anyway, so I won't ride north. Since I'm rich already, I don't need to ride east. I'm looking for adventure, so I'll go to the west. I'm not afraid to die, and in any case, I'm an old man."

He turned his horse round and
rode westwards.   After riding for two
hours, Ilya saw a black castle in the
distance.   Although he did not know it,
a band of robbers lived there.

From the highest tower a lookout
saw Ilya riding towards the castle.

"I can see an old man riding a white
horse," he shouted to the others.

The robbers hurried from the castle, and Ilya saw them running down the hillside towards him. He stopped his horse, sat very still, and waited.

The robbers drew their knives, so Ilya drew his sword.

"Get off your horse and give us your silver and gold," shouted the leader of the robbers.

Ilya sat still for a moment longer before shaking his head.

"No," he replied. "You can't have either my money *or* my horse."

Six robbers rushed at the old knight, their knives raised, but not one of them could get near him. His sword flashed in the sunlight, and six robbers lay dead on the ground.

"Oh dear," said Ilya. "You've got to be better than that if you want my gold and silver."

Another ten robbers rushed towards him, and once again he showed just what

a fine swordsman he was. This time,
ten robbers lay dead on the ground.

"What's the matter?" teased Ilya.
"Don't you want my horse? Or my
silver and gold?"

The robbers became very angry.
They did not like being teased.

"You can't be very good robbers,
for I'm only an old man," laughed Ilya.

With a great shout of anger, the
rest of the robbers rushed at him.
Ilya spurred his horse forward, and his
sword flashed swiftly to left and right,
until every single robber lay dead.

Never again would they kill and rob passing travellers.

Now that he had made the road safe, the old knight turned his horse and rode back to the crossroads. With one blow of his sword he cut down the signpost that pointed to the west.

Then he looked at the other two signposts.

"I'm already rich, so I won't ride eastwards. Although I don't wish to be married again, I think I will ride towards the north. Perhaps I'll have more adventures," he said to himself.

By now it was late afternoon, and Ilya's horse was tired. As he rode slowly along, the sun sank lower in the sky, and he wondered where to sleep that night. Just as it was growing dark, he saw a beautiful white castle on a hillside beside the road.

Ilya did not know that a wicked witch lived in the castle. She saw

him riding slowly along the valley,
and she changed herself into a
lovely young woman, dressed in a
white gown. Then she ran to meet the
old knight.

"Welcome to the white castle!" she said
in a soft pretty voice. "You look tired!"

"I have travelled far," said Ilya.

"Then please stay the night. I
have the finest food and the softest
beds in the land," said the witch.

They left his horse in the stable, and the witch led Ilya to the great hall. Supper was laid before him, and Ilya ate happily. Never before had he tasted such good food. Each dish seemed to have been freshly cooked, although he did not see any servants.

When he had eaten, the lovely young girl led him to his room. As they walked through the castle, Ilya could see that they were alone. There were no servants or soldiers, and he could not understand it.

"It's strange," thought Ilya, "that this pretty young lady is all by herself in a great castle. I wonder if she can be a witch?"

When they reached the room where Ilya was to spend the night, she opened the door and pointed to the bed.

"See," she said. "This is the softest bed in all the land. Lie down on it and see just how soft it is!"

Ilya looked down at the bed. He was very tired indeed, and the deep pillows and the thick bedclothes looked softer than any other bed he had ever seen.

"Lie down and sleep," said the witch softly.

"Let me see you try the bed first," cried Ilya, and lifting her up he threw her heavily on to the soft bed. She screamed as she fell, and suddenly the bed, the pillows, the thick bedclothes *and* the witch disappeared through a hole into a dungeon far below, and she was never seen again.

Near where the bed had been, Ilya
saw a bunch of keys that the witch
had dropped as she fell.   He picked
them up and went to open the dungeons.
There he found many travellers who
had been tricked by the witch.

"Thank you!" they all cried as
they came out.   "You have saved us all."

Next morning Ilya rode back to
the crossroads.   With his sword he cut
down the signpost pointing to the
north, then he looked at the last
signpost.

He said to himself, "I shall ride
to the east. I don't want to be any
richer, but it's the only road I
haven't ridden along."

He galloped for three hours along
the road to the east, then the road
became a narrow path. On one side
a steep cliff rose high above him,
on the other there was a sheer drop
to a valley far below.

Now he rode along more slowly,
until he was stopped by a huge rock
which lay right across the path.
There was no way round it.

Ilya got off his horse, gripped
the rock with both hands, and tried
to move it, but it was much too heavy.

He looked at it again, and thought
hard. Then he put his back against
the cliff, and, using all his strength,
raised the rock at one side. He
raised it higher and higher, until
suddenly it tipped over and fell into
the valley below.

When Ilya sat down to rest for a
moment, he saw that there, where the
rock had been, was a hole full of
boxes and sacks.

"What's in these?" he wondered,
and he opened the boxes. They were
full of gold! And when he opened
the sacks, they were full of silver!

"I've got all the gold and silver
I want," said the old knight. "I must
find someone who needs it."

For many weeks Ilya rode through the
countryside looking for poor people.
To each one that he found, he gave some
silver and some gold. When he had given
away all he had found, he rode back to
the crossroads, and with one blow of
his sword, he chopped down the
last signpost.

And from that day on, all the roads
were safe for travellers, thanks to
Ilya of Muron.

Tobias and the Angel

Tobit was a very good shopkeeper.
People came from far and wide to buy
his goods. He made a great deal of
money, and he lived with his wife in
a big house, with many servants.

Everyone thought well of Tobit
and his wife Anna, for they were very kind
people. Whenever Tobit discovered
that one of his friends was in trouble,
he would lend him money, or let him
stay at his house.

All this changed when Tobit
suddenly went blind. He could no
longer work in his shop, and the
friends he had helped in the past
forgot to pay back the money he had
lent them. Even the king and the
royal family forgot to pay their bills.

Tobit and Anna became poorer and
poorer. The servants left, and the

big house had to be sold.

The only joy they had was their
baby son, Tobias.

As the years passed, he grew up
to become a strong, handsome young man.
But his mother would hardly let
him out of her sight, in case
something happened to him!

One day a stranger knocked at
their door. He had brought a
basket of food for them, and Anna

was worried. Why should an unknown man bring them food? The stranger said his name was Azarius.

"Do stay for a meal," said Tobias, who was just as kind as his father. "We don't have many visitors these days."

As they were eating, their guest noticed a carved wooden chest in one corner of the room.

"What a beautiful chest!" said Azarius.

"It's all we have left of our old home," said Anna.

Tobias opened the chest to show Azarius that the inside was also beautifully carved.

"We only keep a few things in it now," said Anna.

"Like Mother's wedding dress!" said Tobit.

Tobias lifted it out to show it to Azarius, and as he did so, a piece of paper fell on the floor.

"What's that?" cried Anna.

Tobias looked at it.

"Who is Ruben?" he asked. "This piece of paper says that someone called Ruben owes us money."

"Oh yes! So he does!" said his father. "But he lives in Persia now, and it takes two weeks to get there. It's a long way to walk."

"Ruben sells carpets, doesn't he?" asked Azarius.

"That's right," said Tobit. "Why?"

"I've heard he's made a lot of money," was the reply. "I'm on my way to Persia. Why not let your son Tobias come with me and collect the money that Ruben owes you?"

"Yes, please let me go," cried Tobias.

"That's a good idea!" said Tobit.

His wife Anna was not so happy about it, but early next day Tobias and Azarius set off for Persia.

It was a long and difficult journey walking across the hot desert.

When they had been walking for some days, they came to a wide river.

"Why not have a swim?" said Azarius. "It will cool you down."

Tobias could not swim very well, but he went into the river. It was cool and pleasant, and he began to enjoy himself.

Then suddenly he saw a huge fish swimming towards him.

"Help! Help!" he cried. "Save me, Azarius!"

"Take the fish by the gills, and lift it from the water," replied Azarius.

Tobias was very frightened, but
when the fish came closer he grabbed
it with both hands, then lifted it
out of the water.

"Bring it here and we'll have it
for supper," shouted Azarius.

Tobias waded ashore, still holding
the fish by the gills. They lit a
fire, and Azarius cleaned the fish
with his knife. He took out the
fish's liver and gall bladder, and
gave them to Tobias.

"Keep these in your pack," he said.
"Wrap them carefully, because we'll
need them later."

Tobias did as he was told, although
he thought it was a strange thing to ask.

A week later the two travellers
arrived in Persia, and soon they found
Ruben, who gave them a great welcome.

"Of course I remember old Tobit!
I'm sorry to hear he's not doing so
well. I owe him a lot of money," he
said. "You must take it to him."

He insisted that the two travellers
stayed with him. He took them to his
house, where they rested until it was
time for the evening meal.

Tobias slept for a little while.
When he woke up, he found Azarius
sitting at the foot of his bed.

"I've something to tell you,"
said Azarius.

"What is it?" asked Tobias.

"I must give you a warning.

Ruben has a very beautiful daughter called Sara, and some time ago a demon fell in love with her. Of course he can't marry her, so he has said that no one else is going to be her husband. Already Sara has been married seven times, and each time the bridegroom died on his wedding night."

"Seven bridegrooms and all dead!" exclaimed Tobias.

"And you are to be her eighth bridegroom!" said Azarius.

"Don't be silly," cried Tobias. "I'm not going to marry a girl I've never seen!"

And he turned over and went back to sleep.

That evening they met Sara, who was the sweetest and most beautiful girl that Tobias had ever seen.

"Demon or no demon, I'm going to marry her," he told Azarius.

And Sara had fallen in love with Tobias the moment she saw him.

Her father did not want them to marry.

"You will die if you marry Sara," he told Tobias. "You are my old friend's son, and I can't let you do it."

But Tobias and Sara would not listen to him.

On the day before they were to be married, Azarius took Tobias to one side and said,

"You remember I told you to keep that fish's liver? Now it's time to use it. Tonight, just before you go to bed, put it on the fire. Then stay in your room until dawn."

"It's a very strange thing to ask," said Tobias, "but I'll do it."

That night before he went to bed, Tobias took the fish's liver and put it on the fire. Then he went to his room.

Soon a most dreadful smell filled the
house, as the fish's liver burned.
When the demon came to kill Tobias,
the smell stopped him entering the house.

As the demon stood angrily at the
door, he suddenly saw Azarius, and
rushed to attack him.

Now Azarius was really an angel,
and angels hate demons. He fought the
demon all night long. Lightning
flashed across the sky as they battled,

and thunder roared. Then as the sun
rose, the demon was beaten. He
disappeared and was never seen or
heard of again.

Of course Tobias was still alive
next day, and Ruben was very pleased.

Sara and Tobias were married, and
the wedding party went on for days.
Then it was time for Tobias to
return to his parents with his
beautiful bride.

When they left, Ruben gave them
many presents of gold and silver.
They did not have to walk back.
They rode on camels, as did their
many servants.

No one was more surprised than
Tobit and Anna when Tobias returned
home. They had been sure he had died
in the desert, or been attacked and killed
by bandits.

Anna told her poor blind husband
how beautiful Sara was, and Tobit wept
tears of joy.

Then Azarius came forward.

"Tobias," he said, "go and fetch the
fish's gall bladder, and wipe it over
your father's eyes."

Tobias trusted Azarius, but he still
thought it was a very strange thing to
ask. The moment he touched his father's
eyes with the gall bladder, Tobit was
able to see.

"I can see! I can see!"
he cried joyfully.

It was the most wonderful day
the family had ever known. Tobias
had come home, he had brought a lovely
bride, Ruben had sent all the money

he owed them, and now Tobit could
see once more.

For a while the family forgot about
Azarius in their happiness.

Tobias was first to remember.

"We must thank Azarius," he said,
looking round. "Where is he?"

They saw him a little way off,
smiling at the happy family. Then he
seemed to grow wings, and flew high
into the sky.

"Now I know," said Tobias. "He's
my guardian angel!"

The Sword
in the Stone

*There are many stories about
King Arthur and his life.
The next two stories are about
the two swords that helped to
make him famous.*

*This first story tells of how
he got his first sword.*

The story starts when Arthur's
father, the King of Britain, became
ill. He sent for his friend Merlin,
who was the chief wizard in the
country and much feared for the
magic he could work.

The king said to him,

"I know I'm going to die soon.
I want my son to be safe from
my enemies. Take him away and hide him
until he is old enough to become king."

That night Merlin rode away from
the castle with the king's baby son,
and left him with a knight and his
family. There the boy grew up into
a fine young man.

After the old king died, there
was no king in Britain for a long
time. There were many lords who
wanted to be king, and they fought
one another, but none of them was
powerful enough to become king.

At last, when Arthur was fifteen,
Merlin decided it was time for him to
take his place as king, and he brought
him back. Then Merlin sent for all the
lords who wanted to be king, and the
knights from all over Britain.

One by one they arrived at the

royal castle, bringing their followers.
Soon there was a great gathering of
knights and lords, all wondering what
Merlin had to say.

And there, in the courtyard, as
they arrived, they saw a huge black
stone, with a sword driven deep into it.

They could not go very close to it,
for it was guarded by soldiers, but
they could see there were some words
written on the stone.

When all the knights and
lords had gathered in the courtyard,
Merlin came to them. He sent the
soldiers away, then read out the words

on the stone so that all could hear.

"He who pulls the sword from the stone shall be King of Britain."

There was silence for a few moments then, one by one, each knight and each lord tried to pull the sword from the stone.

But no matter how hard they pulled, the sword never moved.

At last they stood silent once more, angry that they had failed.

Only Arthur had not yet tried. No one knew that he was the old king's son, and some of the knights began to laugh when the young lad walked up to the stone. How could he succeed where all the strongest men in the land had failed?

Then, without a word, Arthur took hold of the sword's handle, put one foot against the stone, pulled—and the sword came free.

There was a gasp from the crowd.

Then they began to cheer. They had
a king once more!

Merlin told them that Arthur was
the son of the last king, and that he
had hidden the young prince until he was
old enough to become king.

Soon afterwards Arthur was crowned,
and the people of Britain were happy
to have a king to lead them once more.

Excalibur

One day King Arthur and Merlin
were riding through the forest
when they met a knight. He was
sitting on his horse right in the
middle of their path and they could
not get past him.

"You can't come past without
fighting me!" shouted the knight.

"Then I will fight you," said
King Arthur, drawing his sword.

Merlin stood back to watch as
the two men prepared to fight.

The knight was much taller than
Arthur. He looked as if he might
win easily, but Merlin knew that
Arthur was quick and light on his feet.

Each time the knight swung his
sword, he missed. And each time
he missed, Arthur jabbed him with
his sword—again and again.

The knight became more and more

angry. He turned quickly, the two
swords met, and there was a loud
crack. Arthur's sword had snapped
in two!

The knight raised his sword to
kill Arthur, who was now at his
mercy. In that moment, Merlin cast
a spell and the knight stood still,
his sword still raised, unable to move.

"I could not let him kill you,
my lord," Merlin said to Arthur.
"You can finish the fight later."

"I'll have to go back to the castle to get another sword," replied the young king.

"There's no need to return to the castle. I know where a sword is waiting for you," said Merlin mysteriously.

He led the way through the woods until they came to a lake. As they walked to the water's edge, an arm rose out of the water. It was dressed in white silk, and it held up a sword.

Even as the two men looked, a boat came to the shore, carrying a beautiful young lady with long golden hair.

"This is the Lady of the Lake," said Merlin, as she stepped from the boat.

Arthur bowed low, and she spoke to him in a soft voice.

"The sword you can see is for you,"
she said. "Only you can use it.
It is called Excalibur,
and it will serve you well until you
are an old man. But before you die,
you must return it to me."

"I will return it," promised Arthur.

He and Merlin stepped into the boat
and rowed out to the middle of the
lake. Arthur took the sword, and
the arm which had held it sank silently
beneath the water.

"Now you have a sword, you can
return to your fight with the knight
in the forest," said Merlin.

They went back to where the knight

was still standing like a statue.
Merlin removed the spell he had cast,
and with a shout the knight rushed
at Arthur.

He fought well, but Arthur and
Excalibur fought better, and at last
Arthur knocked him to the ground.

"Mercy!" cried the knight. "You
may pass me."

"And so shall everyone else,"
cried Arthur. "You must promise to
let all travellers pass through the
forest, or I will kill you now."

"I promise, my lord, I promise," said
the knight, and King Arthur let him
go free.

Arthur was even more proud of his
sword now that he had used it in
battle. Excalibur saved his life many
times after that.

*   *   *   *   *   *

After many years, when Arthur was

old and lay dying, he handed Excalibur
to one of his knights, saying,

"Take my sword and cast it
into the lake."

The knight took the sword away.   As
he rode towards the lake he looked at
Excalibur and saw how beautiful it was.

"It's far too good to throw into a
lake," he said to himself.   "I shall
keep Excalibur, and tell the king that
I threw it into the lake."

He hid the sword beneath a bush,
then he went to the king.

"Tell me," said Arthur.   "Tell me
what happened."

"It sank into the water," said
the knight.

"Then you did not cast Excalibur
into the lake!" cried the dying king.
"Now do as I have asked."

The knight went back to where he
had hidden the king's sword.   Once
again he looked at it and thought,

"It's much too good to throw into
a lake." So once more he hid it.
Then he returned to the king.

"Did you cast Excalibur into the
lake this time?" asked Arthur.

"Yes," said the knight. "I threw
it into the water, just as you asked."

"And what happened?" asked the king.

"It fell into the water and sank
with a great splash," replied the knight.

King Arthur became very angry.

"Do I have to get up from
my death bed and cast it
into the water myself?" he shouted.
"Now do as I have asked."

The knight was very ashamed.

Quickly he went back and found the
sword.   Then, with all his might, he
cast Excalibur into the middle of
the lake.

The great sword flew through the
air.   An arm dressed in white silk rose
from the water and caught it.   The arm
waved Excalibur three times, then
sank beneath the water, taking
the sword with it.

The knight went back to the dying
king and told him what had happened.
Arthur knew that this time Excalibur
had gone back to the Lady of the Lake.

His promise had been kept.

The Monk who Wanted a Pear

Far, far away in the land of China,
there once lived a monk who owned
nothing but a begging bowl and the
clothes he wore.

Every morning after he had said his
prayers in the temple, he went to the
market to beg.

Some people gave him money and
other people gave him food.

One morning when he arrived at the
market, he saw a man with a barrow
full of pears. The monk stopped to
look at the fruit, and he saw that
the pears were ripe and sweet.

"Please will you give me one of
your pears?" he asked the man who
was selling them.

"Go away," replied the man rudely.
"You can't have any of my pears. I've
brought them to market to sell them,

and I won't get any money
if I give them away."

"But I only want one,"
said the monk.

"No," said the man,
turning away.

"You wouldn't miss
just one pear,"
said the monk softly.

"Go away!" shouted the man.

"But you've got a whole barrowful
of pears. *Please* give me one,"
begged the monk.

"No, no, no!" shouted the man
rudely. "Go away. I won't give you
even one pear. Go away!"

People near by came to see what was
happening when they heard the noise.

"Do give him a pear," said a woman.

"No," said the man. "Why should I?"

Other people began to ask him to
give the monk a pear, and the man
began to shout at them as well.

Then a tall man took some money
from his purse and paid for a pear.
He gave it to the monk, who was very
pleased.

"Thank you," said the monk to the
tall man. "That's very kind of you.
Now if you wait a moment, I'll give
you some of *my* pears."

The tall man looked at the monk in
surprise.

"If you have pears of your own,"
he asked, "why did you beg for one?"

"Because I needed some seed," replied
the monk.

Everyone watched as he ate the pear
until only the seeds were left. Then
he dug a small hole in the earth with
his heel and planted one of the seeds.
He covered it with soil, and asked for
some water.

There was no water, but someone in
the crowd had a cup of tea. He gave
it to the monk, who poured it carefully

on to the soil where he had planted
the seed.

As the crowd watched, they saw the
soil begin to move. A tiny green
shoot appeared, and as they watched
it got bigger. Quickly the shoot grew
into a small plant, then into a tall
tree. Green buds appeared on the
twigs, and these became leaves.

As the leaves grew larger, pink and
white buds appeared and changed into
blossom. When the blossom began to
fall, the crowd could see a crop of
tiny pears upon the tree.

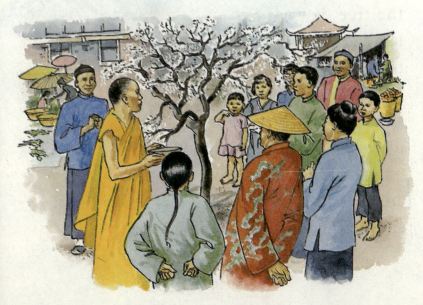

Soon the pears were ripe, and the monk climbed up the tree to pick them. He began to give them away to the people who were watching.

At last, when he had given away all the pears, he climbed down from the tree.

Among the crowd standing round the tree, there was a woodman with an axe.

"May I borrow your axe?" asked the monk.

"Of course you may," replied the woodman.

The monk took the axe from him and chopped the tree down. He handed the axe back to the woodman, lifted the tree on to his shoulder and carried it away.

For a short while the crowd talked to one another about what they had seen.

The man who was selling pears went
back to his barrow.   It was empty!
There was not one single pear left!

"That monk has given away all my
pears!" he shouted angrily.

As he had no pears to sell, he
decided to go home to get some more.
But when he went to push his barrow,
the handles had gone.   Someone had
chopped them off!   He was so angry
he could not even speak.

Then he heard the crowd laughing
at him.   Just one or two at first,
then more and more, louder and
louder, until the market place rang
with their merriment.

Since that day, every time the monk
comes to market, the man with the
barrow always gives him the biggest
and best pear, before he can even ask.
Because the man with the barrow
does not want to see any more of
the monk's magic!

Unnana and the Elephant

Once upon a time, in the forests
of Africa, there lived a woman called
Unnana, who was very poor.

She had two children who were so
beautiful that people would stop
to look at them.

One morning Unnana saw that there
was very little firewood left.

Without firewood she would not be
able to cook. She called to her
children and said,

"I'm going into the forest to get
some firewood. While I'm away,
your cousin Mona will look after you."

When Mona arrived at the house,
Unnana left the children with her,
and went off to the forest.

For a time the children and their
cousin played outside their house
in the shade of a tree.

Suddenly Mona looked up into the
branches and saw an ape staring
down at them.

"Whose children are these?"
asked the ape.

"They are the children of Unnana,"
replied Mona.

"They are very beautiful," said the
ape. "I've never seen such beautiful
children before."

He stared at the children for a
minute or two, then without another
word he went off into the forest,
swinging from branch to branch.

When the ape had gone, the children
went on playing. Then a deer walked
from the forest, and stared at the
children with her great soft eyes.

"Whose children are these?" she
asked in a quiet voice.

"They are the children of Unnana,"
replied Mona.

"They are very beautiful," said the
deer. "They are the most beautiful
children I've ever seen."

For a while the deer looked at
Unnana's children, then with one great
leap over a small bush, she bounded
off into the forest.

By now the sun was high in the sky.
The children were tired, so they
sat down at the foot of a tree.

Suddenly a deep voice asked,
"Whose children are these?"

The children looked up to see
a huge lion standing in front of them.

They were all very frightened. For

a moment Mona was too frightened even
to speak.

"They are the children of Unnana,"
she said at last.

"They are the most beautiful
children I've ever seen," said the lion.
As he spoke, his deep voice shook
the leaves on the trees.

He stared at the children for
a minute or two, then softly walked
away into the forest, gently swinging
his tail.

The children were so frightened
that they started to cry for their
mother. Nothing that their cousin
Mona did could stop them crying.

From the forest came a sound.
The children stopped crying for a
moment hoping that their mother was
returning. The sound came nearer, and
they looked up. It was not their mother.

It was a huge elephant with only
one tusk!

The children sat still, too frightened to move.

"Whose children are these?" asked the elephant in a great voice.

"They are the children of Unnana," Mona cried.

"They are the most beautiful children I've ever seen," said the elephant.

For a while he stood still and stared at the children. Mona thought he would go away, just as the ape and the deer and the lion had done. But he did not.

He went closer to the children and said,

"I've never seen such beautiful children before. I will have them."

Without one more word, he opened his great mouth and swallowed both the children. Then he slowly walked away into the forest, knocking down trees and stamping down any small bushes that were in his way.

When Unnana came home from the forest, she could not find either her children or their cousin.

She looked inside and outside the house, and at last she found Mona hiding behind a tree. Mona was so frightened and was crying so much that it was a long time before she could tell Unnana what had happened to her children.

Unnana was very angry.

"Tell me about that elephant," she shouted. "What does he look like, and

where did he go? I must find him
and get my children back."

Mona told Unnana all about the
elephant with one tusk.

Unnana listened, and thought very
hard, then she cooked a big pot
of beans and sharpened her large
cooking knife.

When the beans were cooked, she
placed the pot on her head. Then she
set off into the forest with her knife
in her hand, to find the elephant with
one tusk.

For a while she walked through the forest following the elephant's tracks, until she came to a tree where the ape was sitting in the branches.

"Ape, ape, help me!" she cried. "Which way did the elephant with one tusk go?"

The ape pointed along a path.

"Go along that path until you come to six tall trees with white stones beside them," he said. "There you will find the elephant with one tusk."

Unnana set off along the path. When she had been walking for a while, she met the deer.

"Have *you* seen the elephant with only one tusk?" asked Unnana.

The deer nodded.

"Go along this path until you come to six tall trees with white stones beside them. The elephant with one tusk is near them," she said.

"It seems a long way," said Unnana,

and she went on along the path.

When she had been walking for many hours, she came to a cave with the lion resting outside it.

Holding the knife in her hand, Unnana walked up to him.

"Tell me, lion, where I can find the elephant with only one tusk. He has swallowed my children and I must get them back."

"Go along this track until you come to six tall trees with white stones beside them. The elephant with one tusk is near there," said the lion with a roar.

"It seems a long walk," replied Unnana, setting out once more.

Not long after speaking to the lion, Unnana came to the edge of the forest. There, on the side of a small hill, she saw the six tall trees with white stones beside them, and the elephant with only one tusk.

"At last I've found you," shouted Unnana. "You have swallowed my children."

"Not me!" replied the elephant.

"Elephant, I do not believe you," Unnana said in an angry voice. "Where are my children?"

The elephant did not answer. He just opened his mouth and swallowed Unnana, along with her pot of beans and the knife in her hand.

Down, down, down she went inside
the elephant until she reached its
stomach.

Inside the elephant's stomach
there were so many animals and people
that there was hardly any room left.

There were sheep and goats, cows
and dogs, men and women—and
Unnana's own two beautiful children.
She was very pleased to see them.

"Mother, mother!" cried the
children, running to her. Then they
said, "We're so hungry!"

So Unnana took her cooking pot
off her head and began to feed them.

All the other people who were in the elephant's stomach asked if they could have some.

"The beans are for myself and my children, but there's plenty of meat. Why don't you cook some for yourselves?" asked Unnana.

Then taking her knife, she cut large pieces of meat from inside the elephant. She made a fire and cooked the meat, and soon everyone inside the elephant was happy and well fed.

The elephant with one tusk was *not* happy, however. He could see smoke coming out of his trunk, and he had pains in his stomach.

"I should never have swallowed Unnana," he groaned. "Ever since I swallowed her, I have had pains inside me."

His pains got worse and worse, and at last he died.

As soon as he was dead, Unnana took

her knife and cut a doorway through to the outside world.

Then Unnana, followed by her children, all the men and women, the sheep, the goats, the cows and the dogs, walked out into the sunshine.

They all walked back to the village where Unnana lived. There Mona was waiting for them, and her tears soon dried when she saw they were all safe and sound.

That night they had a great feast of elephant's meat, and all the people who had been inside the elephant thanked Unnana. They gave her so many presents that she and her beautiful children were never poor again.

Rip Van Winkle

*Sometimes legends seem to grow up
in several countries all at the same
time, and sometimes they travel from
one country to another. This story
of Rip Van Winkle started as a
German legend, then it was rewritten
by an American, Washington Irving,
over a hundred and fifty years ago.
He set it in the Catskill Mountains,
which are in the state of New York.*

         *   *   *   *   *   *

Rip Van Winkle lived in a quiet
village beside the Hudson River.

He was a man who enjoyed doing
nothing. He was never happier than
when he was sitting on a rock, just
watching the river flow past.

Sometimes he would fish, but
most of the time he would just sit
and look at the water.

It was so much more peaceful than
being at home, where his wife
nagged at him all the time.

Because he did no work,
his wife complained. She would
tell him to do a dozen different
jobs. When he did do them,
he didn't do them very well
and so his wife complained again.

It seemed to Rip Van Winkle
that she was always shouting at him.

Sometimes, tired of the noise,
he would slip out of the house
to meet a few friends at the inn,
but even there he was not safe.
His wife would often follow him
to the inn, and make him go home
with her.

The only way the lazy man could
get away from her was to take his
gun and go hunting in the woods.
Once he was in the woods, his wife
could look all day and never find him.

So it was, one fine autumn day,
Rip Van Winkle went hunting. All
day long he wandered through the
woods, carrying his gun. He did
not see many animals. Even when
he did, he did not bother to
shoot them.

Gradually the path grew steeper
and when evening came, he had climbed
to the highest part of the Catskill Mountains.

Feeling tired, he threw himself
down on a grassy bank. For a while
he sat looking at the tree-covered
hills and valleys around him, just
enjoying the peace.

Then, as the sun went down, he
heard a voice calling, "Rip Van Winkle!"
And again—"Rip Van Winkle!"

He could tell it was not his wife's
voice, so who could it be?

For a moment he was so frightened
he could not move. Then the voice
called him once more.

This time Rip Van Winkle stood up, and he saw a figure coming towards him through the twilight. It was an old man carrying a barrel on his shoulder.

"Help me to carry this barrel," said the old man.

Rip Van Winkle lifted it from the old man's shoulder and followed him until they came to an open glade.

"Put the barrel down and rest for a while," said the old man. "Now that you've helped me, you must have a drink."

He gave Rip Van Winkle a drink from his barrel, and they drank together as evening changed slowly into night.

And as they sat there in the half-light, strange things seemed to be happening. Rip Van Winkle saw four men dressed in the clothes of a hundred years before, playing

skittles. The men never smiled,
and the sound of the balls hitting
the skittles echoed from mountain
to mountain.

At last, night fell and Rip Van
Winkle fell into a deep sleep. He
slept, and slept, and slept.

*   *   *   *   *   *

When he woke up, Rip Van Winkle
found he was lying on the grassy
bank where he had first seen the
old man. Thousands of dead leaves
covered him, keeping him warm.

He sat up and rubbed his eyes,
and saw it was a bright sunny morning.

"Oh dear," he thought. "I've
slept here all night. My wife will
shout at me again!"

As he scrambled to his feet, he
found that his arms and legs were
very stiff. "I'm getting old,"
he said to himself.

He rubbed his legs, then
started slowly on his way home.

The sun was high in the sky
when he arrived at the village.
As he walked towards it, he thought
there was something strange about it.
What could it be?

He stopped and looked carefully.
There were many new houses, and some
of the old houses had gone! How
could that have happened overnight?

There were quite a lot of people
in the street, but there was no one
he knew.

Rip Van Winkle did not know
what to think.   He stroked his chin
as he looked around—and found to
his surprise that he had a beard
which came half-way down his chest!

He walked more and more slowly as
he drew near to his house.   Every
moment he expected to hear the
sound of his wife's voice, asking
where he had been all night.

When at last he arrived at his
house, he saw to his dismay that
it was falling down, and there
was no sign of his wife.

Rip Van Winkle suddenly felt
thirsty.   He put his hand in
his pocket and found some money.
At least he could go to the inn,
he thought.

But the inn had gone.   A new
hotel stood in its place.

Rip Van Winkle stood on the path
in front of the hotel, feeling unhappy.

He had been followed by a crowd
of children, attracted by his long
beard, rusty gun and strange clothes.
Other people were staring at him too.

"What do you want?" asked a tall man.

"I'm looking for my friends," replied
Rip Van Winkle.

"Who are you looking for?" another
man asked.

"Where is Nicholas Vedder?" asked
Rip Van Winkle.

The people around fell silent. Then an old man replied, "He has been dead for eighteen years."

At that moment a young woman pushed through the crowd with her baby. She wanted to look at the strange man who had arrived in the town. Then her baby started to cry. "Hush, Rip," she said, rocking it gently.

Rip Van Winkle looked up as she spoke, because she reminded him of someone. "What's your name?" he asked.

"Judith Gardener," she replied.

"And what was your father's name?"

"He was called Rip Van Winkle. But he disappeared twenty years ago. He went hunting in the woods and was never seen again."

"And where is your mother?" asked Rip Van Winkle.

"Alas, she too is dead. She died after shouting at a pedlar one morning."

Then Rip Van Winkle told his daughter who he was.

At first no one believed him. They asked question after question, but at last they believed that his story was true.

His daughter took him home with her and he lived in peace happily for the rest of his life. He still enjoyed just sitting on a rock, watching the river flow past.

And sometimes strangers would ask for his story, and he would tell them of that long night's sleep—that lasted for twenty years.

The Sensible Farm Worker

There was once a farmer who was looking for a new farm worker.

Three young men came to see him. After talking to each of them for a while, he could not decide which would be the best worker.

So he asked each of the young men the same question,

"How long can you plough with a stone in your shoe?"

The first young man replied,

"I can work all day with a stone in my shoe."

The farmer went to the second young man, and asked him the same question.

He replied,

"I can work for about half a day with a stone in my shoe."

"How long can *you* plough with a
stone in your shoe?" the farmer asked
the third young man.

"I can't work at all if I get a
stone in my shoe. I would take it
out straightaway," he replied.

The farmer smiled—and the third
young man became his new farm worker.